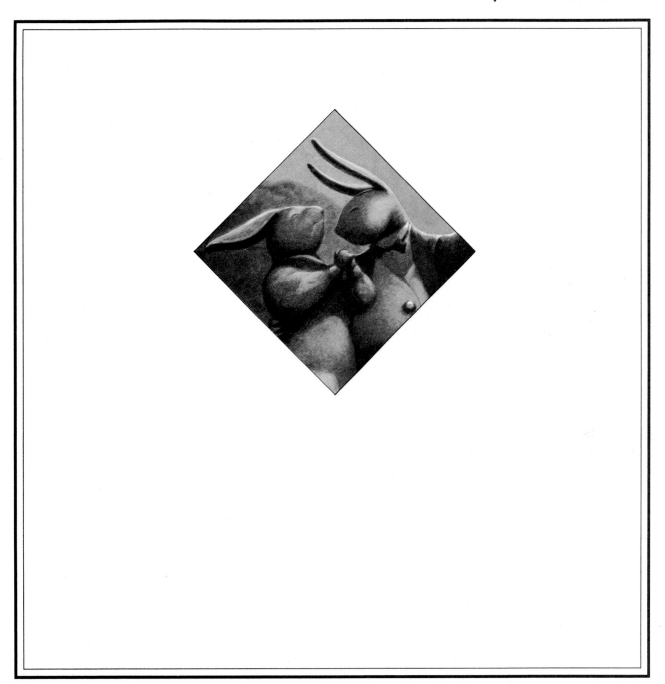

NICHOLAS
CRICKET

NICHOLAS CRICKET

By

Joyce Maxner

Illustrated by

William Joyce

Scholastic Inc.

New York Toronto London Auckland Sydney

ISBN 0-590-44058-6

Text copyright © 1989 by Joyce Maxner.
Illustrations copyright © 1989 by William Joyce.
All rights reserved. Published by Scholastic Inc.,
730 Broadway, New York, NY 10003, by arrangement with
Harper & Row Publishers, Inc.

12 11 10 9 8 7 6 5 4 3 2 1   1 2 3 4 5 6/9

Printed in the U.S.A.   08
First Scholastic printing, March 1991

In memory of Perry and Wendy,
tiny daughters upon whom I often muse
—J.M.

To Marlin and Mary Lane Risinger—
members of that happy breed
who understand the fun
of a moonlight promenade
—W.J.

Nicholas Cricket plays every night
in the Bug-a-Wug Cricket Band.

Moonlight glows and summer wind blows,
rabbits come dancing on tip-tippy toes.
The music is just so grand!

Nicholas Cricket plays with all his might
in the Bug-a-Wug Cricket Band.

Little Lake shines and Little Stream winds,
peep-peep-peepers come dancing through the vines.
The music is just so grand!

Nicholas Cricket is a banjo picker
in the Bug-a-Wug Cricket Band.

Crickets play fiddles and guitars with middles
curvy and round as a rantum riddle
and ducks come dancing
ducky-hey-ducky-diddle.
The music is just so grand!

In the blue blue night
when the moon is bright
underneath the leaves of summer,
if we're quiet and quick
we can find Cricket Nick
and the washboard strummers
and the slap-a-spoon drummers
and the crick-crick-crickety kazoo hummers.

We can dance all night
'til the rosy dawn comes.
The music is just so grand!

Ladybugs strut and toads sashay,
moths and mantises wing their way,
snap-turtles swing and grasshoppers sway
while Nick and the crickets
just
    play
        and
           play.

The music is just so grand!

Then all the Bug-a-Wugs grow sleepy and still
and go back with the moonlight under the hill.
Back to the trees the peepers pop,
back to the hollow the rabbits hop,
back to the willows the weary ducks waddle
and back to our beds our tired legs toddle
to dream as Little Stream
winds
    its way
        into tomorrow.

The music was just so grand!
The music was just so grand!
The music was
just
    so
      grand!